Men's Fitness
magazine

50

MEALS THAT MAKE
MUSCLE

by Ben Ince

Art Editor Rob Lavery
Additional words David Cornish, Joel Snape
Photography packshotfactory.co.uk, Shutterstock
Food styling Georgina Besterman, Karol Gladki
Illustrations Sudden Impact
Subeditor Chris Miller
Art Director Donovan Walker

© Copyright Dennis Publishing
Ltd. Licensed by Felden 2012   **MAGBOOK**

Group Publisher **Russell Blackman**
Group Managing Director **Ian Westwood**
Digital Production Manager **Nicky Baker**
MagBook Publisher **Dharmesh Mistry**
Operations Director **Robin Ryan**
Managing Director of Advertising
Julian Lloyd-Evans
Newstrade Director **David Barker**
Chief Operating Officer **Brett Reynolds**
Group Finance Director **Ian Leggett**
Chief Executive Officer **James Tye**
Chairman **Felix Dennis**

The 'MagBook' brand is a trademark of Dennis Publishing Ltd,
30 Cleveland St, London W1T 4JD. Company registered in England.
All material © Dennis Publishing Ltd, licensed by Felden 2012,
and may not be reproduced in whole or part without the
consent of the publishers.

50 Meals That Make Muscle ISBN 1-78106-030-4
To license this product please contact Nicole Adams on
+44 (0) 20 7907 6134 or email nicole_adams@dennis.co.uk
Printed at BGP, Bicester.

Advertising
Katie Wood katie_wood@dennis.co.uk
Matt Wakefield matt_wakefield@dennis.co.uk

To subscribe to *Men's Fitness* magazine, call **0844 844 0081** or go to **www.mensfitness.co.uk**

CHΔNGE

TO A SUPERIOR PROTEIN

Instant Whey is unlike other whey proteins and the differences can deliver you significant benefits.

166% more bio available cystine, 16% more leucine
It uses Native Whey which is different to conventional whey protein having a less invasive pasteurising process. As a result it contains up to 166% more bio available cystine than conventional whey which is vital for optimal immune function and therefore recovery after exercise. It also contains up to 16% more leucine which helps to build and repair muscle.

It is unbeaten in terms of its protein levels at a guaranteed level of 80%. Containing a market leading protein percentage also means that it contains less fat and less carbohydrate.

Protein percentage		Cost per g of protein	
Reflex Instant Whey inc. Native Whey	**80%**	**2.7p**	
Competitor brand A	78.5%	3.4p	
Competitor brand B	78%	4.6p	
Competitor brand C	76.6%	3.6p	
Competitor brand D	72%	3.8p	

Delivering such a high quality product can only be achieved by controlling the entire manufacturing process and testing each batch produced. Not only does Reflex operate what is arguably the most advanced manufacturing unit in the UK but every single batch of Instant Whey is protein tested and the results published on our website.

Find out more about our products at:

www.reflex-nutrition.com

Given our unique approach to quality we are able to offer a simple, no questions asked Full Money Back Guarantee (see website).

If you haven't tried Instant Whey recently, you owe it to yourself to do so. Not only is it unique in respect of the inclusion of Native Whey, market leading in terms of its protein percentage but it also comes in a range of fantastic flavours and is covered by a simple and effective guarantee.

This explains why we are inviting you to change to a superior protein.

Instant Whey™
inc. Native Whey

Part of our High Protein range

 Please visit & join our Facebook page at Reflex Nutrition Ltd

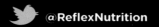 **@ReflexNutrition**

ecotricity

reflex®
Tomorrow's Nutrition Today™

Contents

Welcome   8

Nutrition tips and advice
Food basics   10
Quick tips   17
Food Q&A   20
Supplements   126

Recipes
Breakfast
The 50 recipes start here with a week's worth
of healthy, energy-packed breakfasts   22

Lunch
Sandwiches, salads and wraps
that contain everything you need
to help you hit the gym hard   38

Dinner
Protein-packed meals that will
supplement your workouts and see
you make significant muscle gains   70

Smoothies
These tasty drinks are full of vitamins
and nutrients that will help you recover
from exercise and get stronger   118

Welcome

Ben Ince, editor

I f you want to build muscle, burn fat and get into the shape of your life, what you do in the kitchen is just as important as what you do in the gym.

But that doesn't mean you have to stick to dull but healthy food such as plain chicken and steamed broccoli. With the right ingredients and recipes it's easy to prepare tasty, wholesome meals that will both fuel your training efforts and satisfy your taste buds.

While all the meals in this book are great for building muscle, they're all based on sound nutritional principles that make them equally useful if you want to lose weight or just maintain a generally healthy lifestyle. Understanding these principles will help you to make smart and informed food choices, which is why the first section of the book is dedicated to explaining them in simple terms so you know exactly where you stand.

Then it's straight into the recipes, starting with the breakfast section. Beginning your day with one of these healthy dishes will fuel your morning and keep you feeling full, helping you avoid the temptation to snack on junk food at work.

The lunch recipes include a selection of tasty, simple meals to choose from, so you'll never need to resort to a ready-made sandwich and bag of crisps again. And for dinner there's a large array of delicious, filling and straightforward dishes from around the world that could be prepared with ease by even the most inexperienced chef.

The final recipe section features a selection of mouthwatering smoothies to keep you going between meals. And if you're concerned about whether dietary supplements have a part to play in your eating regime, the book concludes with an explanation of the most effective way to complement your new diet with supplements to get the most out of your training.

So read on, grab your best chef's hat and apron and hit the kitchen!

Food basics

Healthy eating doesn't need to be complicated. Just follow these guidelines to keep it simple

There's no point working hard in the gym if you're going to undermine all your training with poor dietary choices, but knowing what advice to follow can be tricky. Every week sees new fad diets emerge and more scare stories hit the news, while nutritionists and scientists contradict each other on a regular basis. To help guide you through this confusing subject, we've distilled the collective wisdom of the world's leading nutrition experts into the following easy-to-follow guidelines. Memorise them, take them shopping or stick them on the fridge – and then tuck in.

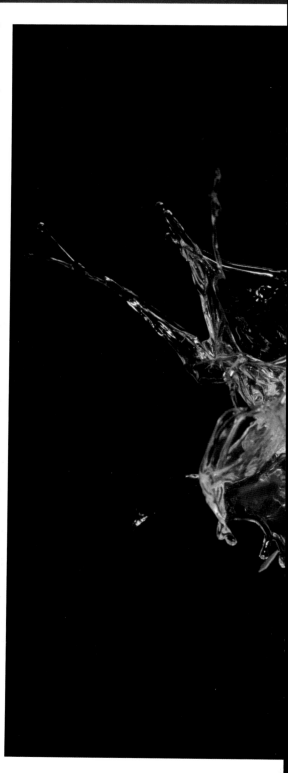

Go free range

Just in case that value crate of cage-raised eggs looks tempting, allow us to remind you that favouring organic and free-range meat and fish is better for your body.

Free-range chickens, for instance, have a more varied diet and get a lot more exercise. This allows the development of more muscle, which tends to contain more zinc, vitamins B, A and K, amino acids, iron, selenium, phosphorus and zinc.

Also, farm-raised salmon have also been found to contain up to eight times the level of carcinogens as their wild brethren, thanks to cramped conditions and poor-quality feed. Grass-fed beef, meanwhile, tends to have much higher levels of conjugated linoleic acid and omega 3 fats than the kind fed on grain and beef tallow.

Eating free range feels less like a frivolous luxury if you think of it this way: it's so nutritionally dissimilar to cage-reared that it's basically different food.

In brief Eat free-range chickens, grass-fed beef and wild-caught salmon when you can. If you don't know where it's from, chances are the answer isn't good.

Stick to real food

Follow this simple rule of thumb: only eat food that grows in the ground or once had a face. If you do this, you'll end up following all the other rules almost by default.

Alternatively, simply go caveman and think like a hunter-gatherer. When you're looking at something on the shelf, ask yourself if it would have existed 5,000 years ago. If the answer's no, it probably isn't anything that you should be eating.

You may find it easier to stick to the outer aisles of the supermarket, which is where all the fresh produce is usually kept for ease of transportation, and away from the interior where everything's canned, processed or packed full of preservatives. Avoid things containing preservatives that you can't spell or ingredients you wouldn't keep in the kitchen; eat things that will rot eventually, so that you know they're fresh.

In brief Eat food, not products pretending to be food.

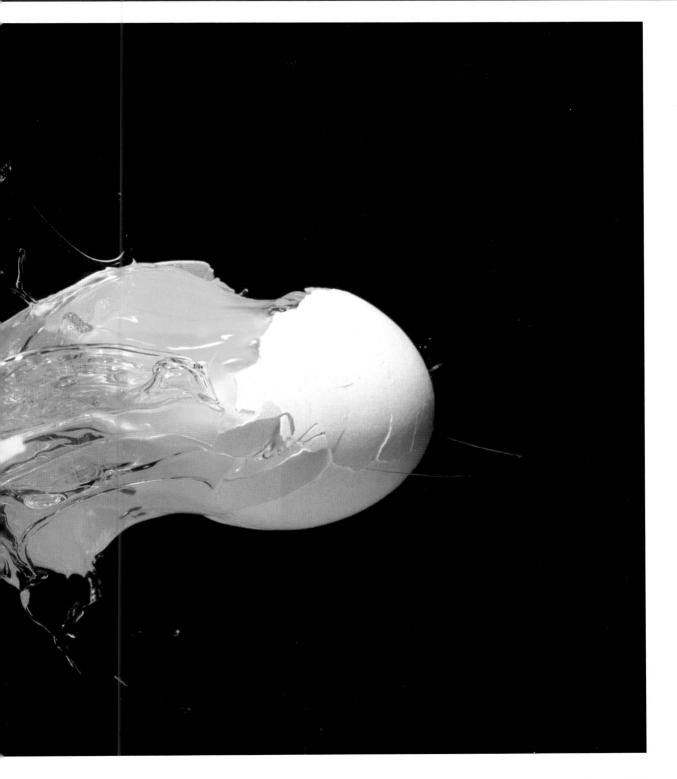

Veg is king

There's no such thing as too much veg, especially if you're talking about vegetables grown above ground. Regardless of what else you're eating, your plate should be about half-full of them.

The Food Standards Agency's 'eatwell plate', which has replaced the traditional food pyramid as the government-endorsed illustration of what to eat, suggests that roughly a third of your diet should come from fruit and veg. But it also suggests that another third should be made up of 'bread, rice, potatoes and other starchy foods'.

This is not the way to a hard, lean body, because the fundamental problem with starchy carbohydrates is they cause sudden and prolonged rises in blood sugar, which is known to provoke biochemical imbalances that predispose you to weight gain, type 2 diabetes and other nasty health problems.

Besides, there's nothing in starchy carbs that you can't get elsewhere. Carbohydrate is a prime energy source that you should eat – but in the form of more nutritious carbs with slower sugar release, which is the type you get from pretty much every vegetable apart from the potato.

You'd have to eat half a kilo of asparagus to ingest the same amount of carbs as you get in a single wholemeal pitta bread. If you want to get lean to show off your abs, keep that in mind.

It's also an oversimplification to put fruit and vegetables together, as the FSA plate does. Yes, they're both good for you, but they're radically different nutritionally. If you're getting your five a day from fruit, your blood sugar levels are going to be going crazy throughout the day thanks to the high fructose content.

In brief Make vegetables the foundation of your diet, along with a maximum of two pieces of fruit a day. Vary them as much as you can.

Don't count calories

Plenty of people still treat the amount of calories you're shovelling in as the only most important thing about the food they eat. That isn't the case. Calories are not a good indication of what a food is like nutritionally and the effect it's going to have on your metabolic rate.

Not convinced? Think of it this way: would you say that a couple of poached eggs are the 'same' as a can of Coke because they contain a similar amount of calories? Us neither.

Also, counting calories makes it too easy to justify bad dietary decisions. Ever heard a friend say that they can eat what they want because they'll burn it off at the gym? They couldn't be more wrong. In fact, the more active you are, the better your nutrition needs to be.

Arguably more important than calorie content is your food's glycaemic load (GL), which indicates how much of a blood sugar spike it'll give you – but manufacturers aren't required to put glycaemic load on packaging.

However, if you're following our guidelines you shouldn't have a problem with this anyway. Steering clear of starchy carbohydrates and sugar means you are already avoiding foods with high GL anyway.

If you do eat high-GL foods, you can also slow the absorption rate – and thereby help prevent blood sugar wobbles – by eating them alongside more protein-heavy foods such as chicken or tuna.

In brief Think quality, not quantities. Eating nutritious food is much better than sticking rigidly to a 2,000-calorie-a-day limit that comes from crisps and toast with jam.

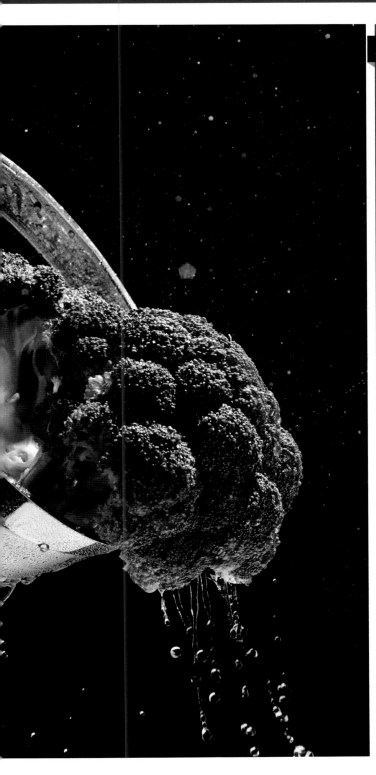

Don't be afraid of fat

Although eating some fat is essential to a healthy diet, it's all too easy to make a mental connection between eating fat and *getting* fat, so many people end up simply skipping it. But that usually means eating something that's worse for you.

One possible reason the government cautions against fat is that it's more calorific, per gram, than carbohydrate or protein. However, if you're worried about your weight it's a good idea to eat foods that are satisfying because you'll eat less of them, which is usually the case with fat. If you replace fat with carbs, meanwhile, you'll get spikes in insulin, which encourage fat storage.

For years we were advised not to eat saturated fat, which was demonised as a cause of unhealthy levels of cholesterol. But this thinking has changed recently. Three major reviews of the subject in the past three years have found no evidence of any link between saturated fats and heart disease. Hydrogenated and trans fats are a different story – research into these sounds alarm bells. But for naturally occurring fats such as those in red meat, avocado and nuts, all the studies suggest there is no cause to avoid them.

After all, humans have evolved to eat saturated fats, so it seems strange that only in the last 50 years have they become bad for us. It is grain, a recent addition to our diets in evolutionary terms, that may not be so easily processed by our bodies.

In brief Avoid hydrogenated fats, especially trans fats. Don't worry too much about the rest.

Lose the booze

Cutting your alcohol intake will have a huge impact on your attempts to lose weight and build muscle.

Consuming large quantities of alcohol adds a huge amount of nutritionally empty calories to your diet. But the problems don't end there: alcohol stimulates your appetite when you're at your weakest – would you really find a doner kebab appealing if you hadn't spent the previous few hours necking pints of lager in the pub? What's more, the inevitable hangover that follows a night on the tiles will leave you feeling far less inclined to train the following day.

Which isn't to say that you shouldn't drink at all. A number of studies have found that red wine in particular offers tangible health benefits, thanks to its high polyphenol content that protects your heart from cardiovascular disease. But don't get too carried away glugging the red stuff – all the studies agreed that consuming more than two glasses a day would negate its positive effects.

In brief Try to cut out alcohol. If you must drink, stick to a glass or two of red wine.

Eat protein with everything

If you're eating to build muscle, you'll probably raise eyebrows at home or in the office with the amount of protein you consume. Someone may even tell you confidently that it can be bad for your health. Here's the truth: the only studies that have ever suggested that protein can cause kidney problems were done on people who already had kidney problems. The studies showing that it's harmful to anyone else simply don't exist.

Protein is one of the most important components of the diet and when you eat a high-protein diet, you're generally less hungry, eat less and lose weight as a result.

So what's the right amount? Estimates from all the way from one to four grams per kilo of bodyweight, per day, but most nutritionists agree that two grams is the minimum. As for how much you can digest at one sitting, a 2009 Canadian study found that roughly 20 grams was the limit for increasing the body's protein synthesis (raising the amount you can use) so there's no point having more than that – though the study focused specifically on egg proteins, so others might behave differently.

So what does this boil down to when you're making your dinner? Stick to a two-to-one ratio of vegetables to protein in every meal, by sight.

In brief It's almost impossible to eat too much protein, although you could easily not be getting enough. Eat it with every meal.

Start the day right

Breakfast is vital – skipping it slows your metabolism to a crawl, severely limiting your fat-burning potential. But some breakfasts are better than others – and the Food Standards Agency's advice that you 'base your breakfast on bread or breakfast cereals' and 'wash it down with some fruit juice' is all wrong.

Eating a high-carb breakfast will give you low blood sugar by mid-morning, making you more likely to snack on more high-carb foods, which creates a vicious circle of snacking.

So instead of starting your day with toast or cereal, have something low-carb that's more nutritionally rounded. We'd suggest plain full-fat yoghurt with berries and nuts, or scrambled eggs with smoked salmon or ham.

Alternatively, just see off whatever's in the kitchen because last night's leftovers are one of the best (and cheapest) things you can eat, assuming you're eating right in the first place.

In brief Think of breakfast like any other meal: you need a blend of protein, fats and fruit or veg. And there's no law stopping you from eating curry.

wellman®

"I have been taking **Wellman**® for many years now and I just don't feel the same when I'm not using it. Anyone competing or living a healthy lifestyle needs **Wellman**® in their life. I'm a champion and I recommend it."

Ashley Theophane

Ashley Theophane
- *British Champion 2011 - 2012*
- *World Welterweight Champion (GBC)*
- *International Champion (IBO)*
- *Welterweight World Number 4 (IBF)*

Wellman® Original tablets   Wellman® Sport tablets   Optimuscle® Ultra Whey Protein *

Wellman® is an advanced range of nutritional products, tailored to the specific requirements of men. It has helped top athletes like **World Champion boxer Ashley Theophane** stay ahead of the game and competing or not, it could do the same for you.

www.wellman.co.uk

VITABIOTICS
WHERE NATURE MEETS SCIENCE

Wellman® *tablets from Boots, Superdrug, supermarkets, Holland & Barrett, Lloyds, pharmacies &, health stores*

***Optimuscle**® is available at GNC and www.vitabiotics.com*

Vitamin supplements may benefit those with nutritionally inadequate diets.

Follow us on:
@VitabioticsUK
facebook.com/Vitabiotics

Quick tips

Form and maintain good eating habits with these helpful hints

Go frozen

Buying frozen veg in bulk is cheap and convenient. What's more, the amount of nutrients lost in the freezing process is roughly the same as the amount lost from fresh veg as it's transported from field to shop to kitchen, so it's no less nutritious.

Keep junk far away

Proximity is one of the biggest factors influencing men's snacking habits, according

to a University of Belfast study. So keep healthy snacks in your drawer at work to avoid the temptation of the vending machine.

Shop frequently

Buy fresh food on your way home from work every couple of days, rather than doing a weekly shop. That way you'll have limited options to choose from, which will make you more likely to opt for the nutritious ones, according to a study from the *Journal Of Consumer Psychology*.

Forward plan your food

Batch-cooking healthy meals in advance can save you time and hassle over the course of the week. Having prepared meals also means you'll be far less likely to eat out, ensuring you retain control over exactly what you eat.

Use the hunger/ fullness scale

Imagine your hunger on a scale of one to ten, where you're starving at 1, mildly hungry at 3, comfortably full at 7 and stuffed at 10. If you make sure you eat whenever your hunger reaches 3, but always stop when it hits 7, you're far more likely to keep your blood sugar levels stable.

Measure your portion sizes

It can be tempting to pile your plate high with food, especially after a hard training session, but regulating your portion sizes is important no matter what you're eating – especially if you're trying to lose weight.

Think healthy

It may sound a bit silly, but simply thinking healthy thoughts

before deciding what you want to eat can make it neurologically easier to exercise self-control when making food choices, according to a study published in the *Journal Of Neuroscience*.

Give yourself an eyeful

If the fridge shelf closest to your eye level is full of fruit and veg, you're 2.7 times more likely to choose something healthy to eat, an American study found.

Eat spicy foods

Choosing the hottest thing on the menu isn't just a dubious way to impress the ladies. The high levels of capsaicin found in spicy foods has been shown in a number of studies – including one from the *Journal Of Biological Chemistry* – to ramp up your metabolic rate, which causes the body to burn more calories.

WWS
WINNING WAYS SPORTS

DID YOU KNOW?

WWS Sell More Creatine Tablets Than Any Other Company In The UK!

FACT

Protein+
Great tasting, high quality whey protein blend. Containing Creatine Ethyl Ester & L-Glutamine.
For Muscle Growth & Definition.
£19.99 per 908g Tub

Tribulus Terrestris
Research has shown that when taking Tribulus Terrestris it can *increase your testosterone levels* by up to 50%.
£9.99 per 90 Capsules

EXTRA STRENGTH
THERMO BURN Xtr
EXTRA WARNING STRENGTH

Weight Manager, Carb Blocking & Energy Boosting

- 600mg Citrus Aurantium
- 200mg Green Tea
- 100mg Cayenne Pepper

Creatine Monohydrate
It is a natural source of energy for muscle contraction during high intensity exercise. *To help you train harder for longer*
£4.99 per 60 x 1000mg Tablets
£14.99 per 250 x 1000mg Tablets

Thermoburn Xtr - Feel The Burn!
The Worlds Fastest & Most Effective Weight Manager
Containing 9 powerful Thermogenic ingredients! Designed to boost your metabolism, massively increase energy, block carbs and *get you ripped*. Caution: Not for under 18's
£19.99 per 90 Capsules

view the full range at: www.wws.co.uk
Tel: +44 (0) 800 085 6211 | Fax: +44 (0) 1254 779201

Prices correct at time of press 1/6/12. - Prices may have changed due to Government Legislations. For up to date prices please visit www.wws.co.uk

Food Q&A

No-nonsense answers to key nutrition questions

Q I've heard that white meat is healthier than red meat. Is this true?

A Chicken and turkey are leaner than beef and lamb and contain fewer calories and less saturated fat, but recent research suggests that neither of these is as harmful to your health as previously thought. What's more, red meat offers a number of additional health benefits, including high levels of fatigue-fighting iron, immunity-boosting zinc and the powerful antioxidant alpha-lipoic acid. It's also packed with creatine and protein, making it one of the best foods for building muscle.

Q What's the difference between good and bad cholesterol?

A Eating foods that are high in hydrogenated fats can raise your levels of low-density lipoprotein (LDL) or 'bad' cholesterol. This causes it to build up on the walls of your arteries and form plaque, a thick, hard deposit that narrows the arteries and makes them less flexible, eventually leading to a stroke or a heart attack. High-density lipoprotein (HDL) or 'good' cholesterol is vital because it removes excess LDL from your artery walls and carries it through to your liver, ensuring that the LDL levels in your blood stream remain at a healthy level. Eating foods rich in omega 3 fatty acids, such as eggs and oily fish, and exercising regularly will help to raise your levels of HDL cholesterol.

Q I've been told that eating carbs late at night will make me fat. Is this true?

A When you eat carbs your body releases insulin, a hormone that is responsible for drawing energy from food into your muscle cells where it is used to rebuild and repair. Any excess energy is stored as fat. That's why it is important to watch your carbohydrate intake around the clock, not just in the evening, no matter what you've been told. Eating too many carbs – especially the sugary type found in snacks and junk food – can result in fat gain in the short term and a host of other serious health problems in the long run.

Q Fruit juice is a healthy option, isn't it? Can I drink as much as I want?

A Ideally you should limit yourself to one glass a day, or better still none at all. Fruit juice is packed with fructose, which will cause your insulin levels to rise and your body to store fat. By drinking fruit juice instead of eating real fruit, you're missing out on a host of benefits, including the filling fibre and variety of nutrients found in the flesh, skin and pith. If you do drink it, eat some healthy fats such as yoghurt, avocado or seeds with it, because most of the vitamins in fruit juice are fat-soluble, meaning they cannot be absorbed by the body without fat.

Q Is there a time when it's beneficial to eat white carbs?

A Eating processed 'white' carbs causes particularly severe insulin spikes. But there is a time when this is desirable: increasing insulin secretion post-workout has been shown to have a powerful muscle-building effect on the body, promoting the synthesis of muscle protein, decreasing muscle breakdown, stimulating glucose uptake for muscle refuelling and improving glycogen storage. So consume high-GI liquid carbs in the form of dextrose after your workout, combined with a quickly-digested protein such as whey isolate.

Q Is there any reason to avoid including dairy in my diet?

A Unless you suffer from lactose intolerance or irritable bowel syndrome, there's no reason why you shouldn't eat dairy products. Cheese and milk are packed with whey and casein, which are the two best sources of protein for muscle building and training support. They also contain key nutrients such as calcium and vitamin D – and they're usually more convenient than other protein sources such as meat or fish. Many dairy foods, such as processed cheese and ice cream, also contain unhealthy ingredients such as trans fats, but having one or two servings of high-quality dairy a day is perfectly fine.

Q Why is it important to drink lots of water and will it help me lose weight?

A Being well hydrated helps to regulate your appetite, which makes you less likely to reach for snacks. Also, downing a glass of water before a main meal can control how much you subsequently eat because it promotes the feeling of fullness so you won't feel the need for seconds. Finally, staying hydrated means you can perform better when exercising, so you can get more out of your sessions. Remember that what we think of as hunger pangs aren't always a signal that you need food; they often just mean that you're thirsty.

Q What's a safe amount of weight to lose in a week?

A It's safe to lose about 1kg a week, although more is fine if you're extremely overweight. It's important to stick to this amount to ensure that you predominately lose body fat and not muscle. This will help you lose more weight because muscle is more metabolically active than fat, so by retaining your muscle mass your metabolic rate will be faster and you'll burn more calories at rest. Following a very low-calorie diet often leads to both fat and muscle loss because the body has to release energy from protein stores once carbohydrate and fat stores are exhausted.

Meat, fish and eggs 3-5 servings

The *MF* food pyramid
Base your daily diet on these recommendations

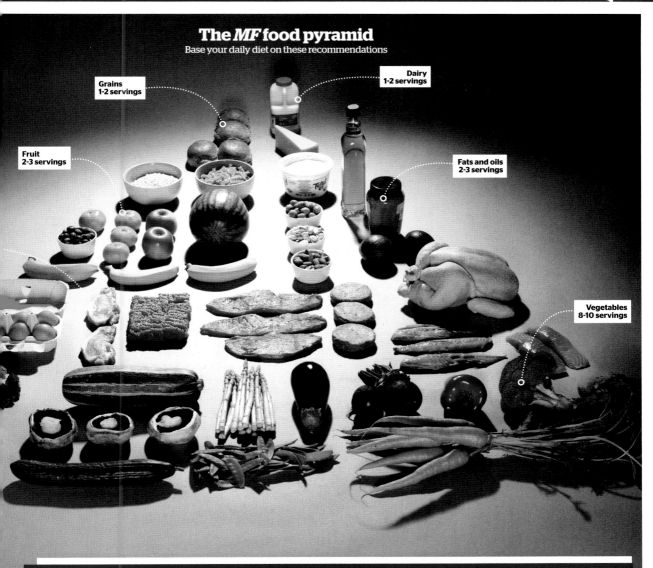

Grains 1-2 servings

Dairy 1-2 servings

Fruit 2-3 servings

Fats and oils 2-3 servings

Vegetables 8-10 servings

Macronutrients The three food types that form the basis of every diet

Carbohydrates
supply you with energy. When you eat carbs, the body breaks them down into its default energy source, glucose. Complex carbohydrates can also provide fibre, vitamins and minerals, which are important for general health. It's best to use vegetables as your main source of carbs instead of grains. If you eat grains, choose the wholegrain or brown variety.

Protein
makes up the structural foundation of all your body's cells, which is why it's crucial to eat plenty of it if you're trying to build muscle. Protein also acts an energy source in the absence of carbohydrates. Animal-based products such as fish, meat, dairy and eggs contain the highest levels of protein, but you can also get it from vegetarian sources such as beans.

Fat
performs a number of key tasks, such as allowing you to absorb vitamins A, D, E and K. There are different types of fat: as a rule, polyunsaturated and monounsaturated fats – found in seeds and nuts – are actively good for you, while the saturated fats in dairy and meat are fine in moderation. Processed trans fats should be avoided at all costs.

Breakfast

Healthy fry-up	24
Home-made muesli	26
Porridge with berries	28
Breakfast burrito	30
Scrambled eggs	32
Turkey omelette	34
Oat pancakes	36

Healthy fry-up (V)

The fry-up is a great British tradition, but it's hardly the most nutritionally balanced start to the day – unless you go for the *Men's Fitness* version, that is. Use the recipe below to whip up a healthy cooked breakfast with ease.

Ingredients

2 eggs
3 slices of avocado
100g baked beans
2 slices of rye bread
2 grilled tomatoes

To make

● Halve the tomatoes and grill them under a medium heat for 3-5 minutes.

● Poach the eggs.

● Heat the baked beans according to the instructions.

● Toast the rye bread and slice the avocado.

Health benefits

Eggs contain all the amino acids needed for muscle growth, and the cholesterol in the yolks helps to produce testosterone.

Rye bread is high in fibre, which will fill you up and help prevent food cravings throughout the morning.

Avocado is packed with heart-healthy unsaturated fats that also help regulate the blood supply to the brain for improved focus.

Nutritional value

429 **calories**
78g **carbs**
17.5g **protein**
10g **fat**

Home-made muesli ⓥ

Making your own muesli at home is quick and easy. What's more, the resulting breakfast is likely to be a lot healthier than the shop-bought variety, because these tend to contain large quantities of sugar.

Ingredients

30g oats
20g barley
30g quinoa
30g raisins
A handful of hazelnuts
A handful of brazil nuts
1 apple, chopped
150ml milk

To make

● Mix all the ingredients apart from the milk together in a bowl.

● Add the milk and serve.

Spice up your muesli

Nutmeg is a great source of tryptophan, an amino acid that the body needs for protein synthesis.

Cinnamon is rich in antioxidants that reduce post-workout muscle inflammation. It also helps to regulate blood sugar.

Ginger can help to boost metabolism by up to 20%, allowing you to burn fat more quickly.

Nutritional value
354 **calories**
45.5g **carbs**
15g **protein**
13g **fat**

Porridge with berries Ⓥ

Oats are the only grains that contain protein, which makes them an excellent breakfast choice if you're looking to pack on muscle, especially if you serve them with other high-protein foods such as nuts and yoghurt.

Ingredients

50g porridge oats
1tbsp Greek yoghurt
A handful of strawberries, chopped
A handful of almonds
100ml milk

To make

● Make the porridge according to packet instructions using the oats and milk.

● Serve with the yoghurt, almonds and nuts on top.

Porridge oats contain wholegrain carbohydrates that are rich in B vitamins, which help build and repair muscle and red blood cells.

Strawberries are high in vitamin C, which increases the production of immunity-boosting white blood cells.

Greek yoghurt has twice the muscle-building protein of standard low-fat yoghurt and just half the carbs.

Other berries you can add

Blueberries are rich in pterostilbene, a compound that helps the body to break down fat and cholesterol.

Raspberries are high in filling fibre, along with calcium and vitamin K, which both strengthen your bones.

Blackberries are a great source of manganese, which helps to eliminate damaging free radicals from the body.

Nutritional value
271 **calories**
25g **carbs**
19g **protein**
12g **fat**

Breakfast burrito Ⓥ

If you're fed up of having the same old breakfast every day, why not try adding some Mexican flavour to your morning meal? This tasty burrito is packed with protein to help you build muscle.

Ingredients

50ml milk
1 egg
A pinch of ground cumin
50g quark cheese
25g black beans
½ red pepper, diced
1tsp coriander, chopped
1tbsp salsa

To make

● Whisk the egg, milk and cumin together, then pour the mixture into a non-stick pan and cook.

● When the egg mixture has almost cooked through, add the red pepper, beans and quark cheese.

● Fold the omelette over and leave it to cook through.

● Serve with the coriander and salsa.

Milk is packed with muscle-building protein and calcium, which helps your body to metabolise fat more efficiently.

Eggs contain all eight amino acids, making them a complete protein source that delays hunger and helps you to build muscle.

Black beans are a great source of fibre, which keeps you feeling full by boosting digestive hormone enzymes that suppress appetite.

Nutritional value
276 **calories**
9g **carbs**
16g **protein**
22g **fat**

Scrambled eggs ⓥ

As a complete protein source containing all eight amino acids, eggs are a great muscle-building breakfast food. Health-conscious eaters used to avoid them, but new evidence shows their high cholesterol has no impact on your blood cholesterol levels.

Ingredients

2 eggs
15g ricotta cheese
1 slice of rye bread
25g spinach
15g butter

To make

● Melt the butter in a saucepan.

● Add the ricotta and eggs.

● Stir with a spatula until the mixture starts to softly set and is slightly runny in places.

● Add spinach and take the mixture off the heat.

● Toast the rye bread while eggs are cooking.

● Give the eggs a final stir and serve.

Health benefits

Ricotta cheese is made from whey protein, which is rich in the amino acids that are critical to building and sustaining new muscle.

Rye bread is high in manganese, which helps to metabolise the protein and good fats from the eggs.

Spinach contains octacosanol, which boosts muscle strength, and phytoecdysteroids, which increase muscle growth.

Nutritional value

532 **calories**
7g **carbs**
62g **protein**
26g **fat**

Turkey omelette

Omelettes are quick and easy to make, and the quality protein found in eggs will help you build muscle and keep you feeling full for longer. Eggs also contain biotin, a vitamin that helps the body to process and burn fat more efficiently.

Ingredients

1tbsp olive oil
3 eggs
15g butter
50g kale, chopped
175g turkey, chopped
25g feta cheese, cubed

To make

● Whisk the eggs in a bowl.

● Heat the oil in a pan, add the turkey, kale and feta and cook gently for around 5 minutes. Set to one side.

● Heat the butter in a frying pan, add the whisked eggs and cook for 3-4 minutes.

● Add the turkey mix and fold over the omelette.

● Cook for a further 2 minutes, then serve.

Health benefits

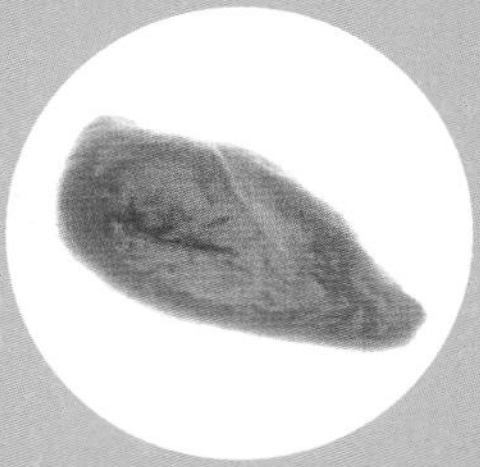

Turkey contains selenium, which helps to strengthen the immune system and defend against harmful free-radical damage.

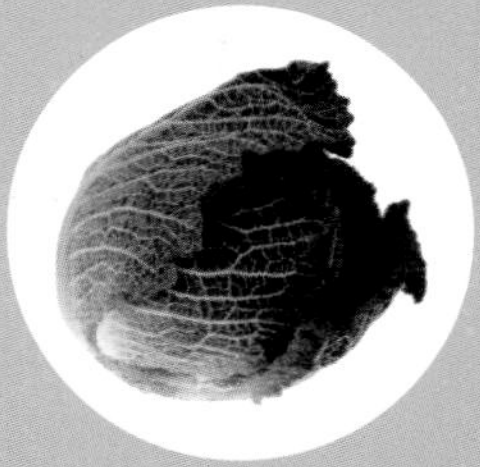

Kale contains phytochemicals that help lower excess oestrogen in the body, thereby promoting muscle growth.

Feta cheese contains muscle-building protein and bone-strengthening calcium.

Nutritional value
610 **calories**
83g **carbs**
25g **protein**
17g **fat**

Oat pancakes ⓥ

Think pancakes are too indulgent to be good for you? With the correct ingredients and preparation, there's no reason why they can't form a delicious, healthy breakfast that will fuel you for the entire morning.

Ingredients

3 egg whites
40g oats
½tsp baking powder
30g caster sugar
Pinch of cinnamon
1tbsp Greek yoghurt
1tsp honey
30g crushed hazelnuts
½ banana, sliced
20g dark chocolate (ideally 80% cocoa)

To make

● Blend the egg whites, oats, baking powder and caster sugar.

● Heat a little butter in a pan and add as much of the egg mix as you want to form a pancake. Cook until it bubbles, then flip and cook for a further 3 minutes. Repeat as required.

● Serve the pancakes with the yoghurt, honey, hazelnuts, banana and a pinch of cinnamon. Melt the chocolate on top to finish

Health benefits

Dark chocolate is loaded with nutrients that help to suppress food cravings, such as tryptophan, serotonin and dopamine.

Greek yoghurt is low-GI, which helps to keep blood sugar levels steady, maintaining energy and reducing sugar cravings.

Hazelnuts contain muscle-building protein and healthy fats, helping to stabilise glucose levels in the bloodstream.

Lunch

Three bean salad 40

Chicken and avocado salad 42

Lemon crab salad 44

Bacon and quinoa salad 46

Tuna salad 48

Turkey salad 50

Beetroot salad 52

Sesame chicken salad 54

Hawaiian toast 56

Chicken wrap 58

Hummus wrap 60

Beef sandwich 62

Egg bagel 64

Turkey bagel 66

Jacket sweet potato 68

Nutritional value
516 **calories**
57g **carbs**
28.5g **protein**
14g **fat**

Three bean salad

It's easy to undo all your hard work in the gym by eating insulin-spiking foods that lead to weight gain. This tasty vegetarian salad is made with low-GI ingredients that will help to keep your blood sugar stable and reduce hunger pangs between meals.

Ingredients

100g kidney beans
100g mung beans
100g cannellini beans
1tbsp olive oil
1 onion, chopped
1 red pepper, chopped
½ lemon, juiced
1tsp parsley, chopped
Handful of baby spinach leaves
Handful of iceberg lettuce
1tbsp cheddar, grated
Pinch of black pepper

To make

● Heat the olive oil in a small pan and fry the onion and pepper on a medium heat for 3 minutes.

● Drain and rinse the beans, add to the pan and cook for another minute, stirring occasionally.

● Remove the pan from the heat and add the lemon juice and parsley. Stir and leave to cool.

● Place the iceberg and baby spinach in a separate container and toss together.

● Place the bean mixture on top of this and finish off with the black pepper and grated cheese.

Health benefits

Kidney beans contain plenty of muscle-building protein and a healthy dose of dietary fibre.

Onion is packed with quercetin, an antioxidant with potent anti-inflammatory properties.

Baby spinach is rich in bone strengthening vitamin K and immunity-boosting vitamin A.

Nutritional value
388 **calories**
12g **carbs**
35g **protein**
14g **fat**

Chicken and avocado salad

Salad might not seem like a muscle-building meal, but with the right ingredients it can be ideal for packing on mass. The chicken in this salad has loads of lean protein to help you build muscle, along with a host of energising B vitamins.

Ingredients

1 chicken breast, grilled and sliced
½ a bag of watercress
½ an avocado, sliced
1 tomato, chopped
¼ of a cucumber, sliced

To make

● Grill the chicken breast until it's cooked through and then cut it into strips.

● Mix the chicken, watercress, avocado, tomato and cucumber in a bowl, and serve with the chicken.

Health benefits

Watercress is rich in muscle fatigue-fighting iron and vitamin B1, which helps your body absorb protein from the chicken.

Avocado is packed with healthy monounsaturated fats and its high levels of fibre will keep you feeling full for longer.

Cucumber provides silica, which maintains healthy tendons and ligaments. Its high water content will help to fill you up too.

Nutritional value
264 **calories**
18g **carbs**
28g **protein**
9g **fat**

Lemon crab salad

Crab meat is rich in muscle-building protein, making it a perfect basis for a tasty lunchtime salad. It also contains plenty of omega 3 fatty acids, which can reduce hunger pangs and help muscle growth.

Ingredients

125g white crab meat
1 bag of mixed salad leaves
½ a red onion, sliced
A handful of black olives
¼ of a cucumber, sliced
A handful of sugar snap peas
1 carrot, grated
1tsp lemon juice
1tsp olive oil

To make

● Mix the bag of salad leaves with the onion, olives, cucumber, sugar snap peas and carrot.

● Top with the crab meat and dress with the lemon juice and olive oil.

Health benefits

Red onion contains chromium, a mineral that helps insulin response, stopping sugar cravings.

Carrots are high in the soluble fibre calcium pectate, which fills you up and binds with acids in the body to reduce cholesterol.

Black olives are a great source of omega 3 fatty acids as well as vitamins A, C and E.

How to shell a crab

Step 1 Remove the tail of the cooked crab (the small triangle at the base of the shell). Pulling it back and snapping it off will expose a small hole.

Step 2 Let the juices drain before rinsing it out with water. Then prise the shell apart by inserting both thumbs into the hole and removing the top section.

Step 3 Use a spoon to scoop out the soft white meat from inside the crab. To get meat from the legs, tear them off and crush them open with the spoon.

Bacon and quinoa salad

Bacon is a great source of slow-release protein, making it ideal for a pre-workout lunch. In addition to drip-feeding your muscles, it also provides plenty of zinc to help fend off tiredness, while the veg will provide you with plenty of energy.

Ingredients

70g quinoa
2 rashers of lean bacon, grilled and chopped
A handful of spinach, chopped
1 red pepper, chopped
1tbsp sesame oil
½ a bag of mixed lettuce
A sprinkle of fresh coriander, chopped

To make

● Place the quinoa in a pan with 180ml boiling water, cover and simmer.

● When the water is absorbed, add the bacon, spinach and peppers to the pan and toss thoroughly in the oil.

● Serve on a bed of mixed lettuce and top with the fresh coriander.

Health benefits

Quinoa is a rich in slow-digesting carbohydrates and the amino acid lysine, which is needed for tissue growth and repair.

Coriander can stimulate the secretion of insulin, helping you avoid energy slumps and hunger pangs.

Red pepper is full of potassium, which helps your metabolism use energy to create muscular growth.

Tuna salad

Tuna is packed with protein and is a hugely popular sandwich filling when mixed with mayonnaise. But for a healthier muscle-building option try mixing it with Greek yoghurt instead and then enjoy it as part of this nutritious salad.

Ingredients

1 can of tuna
2tbsp Greek yoghurt
½ a bag of Swiss chard
1 carrot, grated
1 stick of celery, sliced
½ an onion, sliced

To make

● Drain the tuna and mix it with the Greek yoghurt.

● Mix the Swiss chard, celery, carrots and onion in a bowl. Place the tuna on top and serve.

Health benefits

Celery is high in energy-releasing vitamins B1, B2 and B6. It also contains potassium, which helps curb your salt cravings.

Carrots contain phytonutrients that prevent oxidative damage to the body's cells, inhibiting the growth of colon cancer.

Red onion is full of vitamin C, which maintains the health of your tendons and skin.

Nutritional value

510 **calories**
56g **carbs**
30g **protein**
4g **fat**

Turkey salad

Eating plenty of good-quality protein after training is crucial if you want to build muscle. This turkey salad is brimming with lean protein and iron, making it an ideal lunch to have after a morning workout.

Ingredients

3 slices of turkey, diced
100g couscous
3 spring onions, chopped
1 tomato, diced
½ a cucumber, diced
A sprinkle of chopped parsley

To make

● Prepare the couscous according to the packet instructions then place it in a bowl.

● When cool, mix in the turkey, spring onions, tomato and cucumber.

● Sprinkle with parsley and serve.

Health benefits

Turkey is a lean, low-sodium meat that provides plenty of protein for building muscle.

Spring onion is packed with chromium, a mineral that helps maintain blood sugar levels and control food cravings.

Cucumber contains phytonutrients that are thought to have anti-inflammatory properties.

Talking turkey

100g of turkey breast contains 21.3g protein, 3.3g fat and 107 calories

100g of turkey thigh contains 19.7g protein, 9.1g fat and 117 calories

Nutritional value
491 **calories**
45g **carbs**
20g **protein**
26g **fat**

Beetroot salad ⓥ

This spicy salad will help you to power through your workout and recover quickly afterwards. It provides a decent serving of protein too, despite containing no meat or fish.

Ingredients

80g beetroot, cut into strips
250g baby spinach
1 onion, diced
2 tomatoes
30g raw peanuts
1tsp coriander seeds, roughly milled
1 dried red chilli
½tsp turmeric
1tbsp vegetable oil

To make

● Lightly fry the coriander seeds and the chilli for a few minutes, then crush them with a pestle and mortar and set them aside. Meanwhile roast the peanuts, then crush them and set them aside.

● Heat some oil in a deep pan and cook the chilli, coriander, garlic and onions for 5-6 minutes . Add the turmeric, salt and tomatoes and stir, then add the beetroot.

● Gently fold the spinach into the onion and spice mixture.

● Just as the spinach is beginning to wilt, remove from the heat. Sprinkle the peanuts over, toss gently and serve immediately.

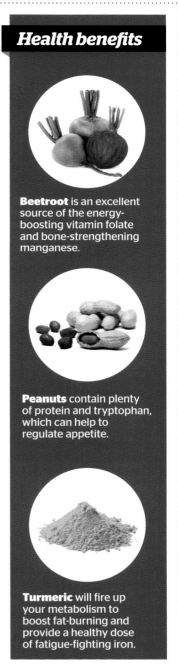

Health benefits

Beetroot is an excellent source of the energy-boosting vitamin folate and bone-strengthening manganese.

Peanuts contain plenty of protein and tryptophan, which can help to regulate appetite.

Turmeric will fire up your metabolism to boost fat-burning and provide a healthy dose of fatigue-fighting iron.

Nutritional value

428 **calories**
15g **carbs**
19g **protein**
14g **fat**

Sesame chicken salad

The paleo diet is based around only eating foods that our caveman ancestors would have eaten, which means cutting out processed foods and refined sugars. This paleo salad has all the key ingredients you need to pack on muscle.

Ingredients (serves 2)

2 chicken breasts
4tbsp sesame oil
2tsp fresh ginger, grated
1 garlic clove, crushed
1 red chilli, seeded and finely chopped
A handful of basil and coriander leaves
½ a red onion, chopped
150g baby spinach
1tsp sesame seeds
5 almonds, chopped
1 mandarin

To make

● Mix the sesame oil, garlic, chilli and ginger in a bowl.

● Slash the chicken in several places and marinade in the sesame oil mixture for 4 hours.

● Add the baby spinach leaves to a bowl with the herbs, onion, almonds and sesame seeds.

● Baste the chicken with the marinade mix and grill for 20 minutes, or until the juices run clear.

● Cut the chicken into strips and add to the salad.

● Dress with the remainder of the sesame oil and mandarin.

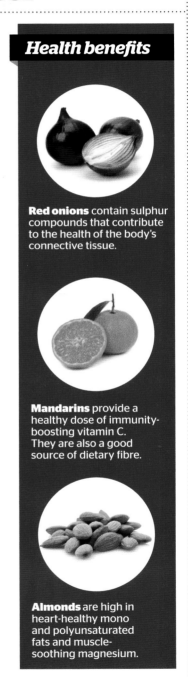

Health benefits

Red onions contain sulphur compounds that contribute to the health of the body's connective tissue.

Mandarins provide a healthy dose of immunity-boosting vitamin C. They are also a good source of dietary fibre.

Almonds are high in heart-healthy mono and polyunsaturated fats and muscle-soothing magnesium.

Nutritional value
279 **calories**
25g **carbs**
17g **protein**
13g **fat**

Hawaiian toast

Ham and pineapple might seem more appropriate on a pizza, but there's no reason why you can't have this Hawaiian staple on toast to liven up your lunch time and fuel muscle growth.

Ingredients

1 slice of wholemeal bread, toasted
1 slice of ham
1 pineapple ring
1 slice of cheddar cheese
A pinch of curry powder
A pinch of pepper

To make

● Lay the ham, cheese and pineapple ring on top of the toast and season with curry powder and pepper.

● Place under a medium to hot grill until the cheese is melted.

Health benefits

Ham contains plenty of protein, iron and creatine, which are the building blocks your muscle need for improved strength.

Pineapple is rich in bromelin, an enzyme which helps your body digest protein and relieve post-training aches and pains.

Cheddar cheese is full of protein and CLA, a naturally occurring fatty acid proven to build muscle and reduce body fat.

Cheesy alternatives

Halloumi is made from goat's milk, which contains less fat and around half the calories of cow's milk.

Mozzarella is a great source of calcium, which is vital for your bones and teeth and helps maintain healthy blood pressure.

Taleggio will keep your bones strong thanks to its high levels of phosphorus, which aids the body's absorption of minerals.

Nutritional value
532 **calories**
62g **carbs**
47g **protein**
11g **fat**

Chicken wrap

This wrap provides plenty of high-GI carbs to fuel your workout, along with the protein in the chicken that will help you build muscle during and after the session.

Ingredients

2 tortilla wraps
150g grilled chicken breast, cut into strips
½ a red pepper, cut into slices
¼ of a cucumber, sliced
A handful of sweetcorn
1 tomato, sliced
1tbsp low-fat mayonnaise
A handful of spinach leaves

To make

● Spread the mayonnaise along the centre of the wraps.

● Place all the other ingredients on top and wrap them up.

Health benefits

Sweetcorn is rich in fibre to help keep your digestive system in good working order.

Cucumber is a source of polyphenols called lignans, which research has linked with a reduction in cardiovascular disease.

Chicken provides a healthy dose of vitamin B6, which is needed for muscle growth and development, as well as protein.

Nutritional value
295 **calories**
38g **carbs**
12g **protein**
11g **fat**

Hummus wrap (v)

This vegetarian wrap provides plenty of high-GI carbs, making it ideal for an instant-energy pre-workout lunch. The hummus also offers easily digestible protein to help you build muscle.

Ingredients

1 tortilla wrap
1tbsp hummus
1tbsp red pepper, diced
A handful of spinach
1tsp black pepper, ground

To make

● Spread the hummus along the centre of the tortilla wrap and place the diced red pepper on top.

● Add the spinach, season with the black pepper and then roll it up.

Health benefits

Hummus is a great source of protein and zinc, which helps the body to manufacture testosterone.

Spinach is packed with iron, which plays a vital role in getting oxygen to your muscles.

Tortilla wraps will help to fend off a mid-workout energy slump due to their high carb content and high glycaemic rating.

Make your own hummus

Ingredients 200g chickpeas, juice of 1 lemon, 2 cloves of garlic, 100ml tahini and 4tbsp water.

To make Put all of the ingredients into a food processor and blend them into a creamy paste.

Extra spice To enhance the taste, try adding 1tsp of cumin, paprika or coriander.

Nutritional value
267 **calories**
40g **carbs**
18g **protein**
6g **fat**

Beef sandwich

Making your own sandwiches is far healthier – not to mention cheaper – than buying them from a supermarket or café. This beef sandwich provides plenty of slow-digesting protein to help you build muscle.

Ingredients

2 slices of sourdough bread
2 slices of beef
1 tomato, sliced
1tsp mustard
A handful of spinach
A twist of black pepper

To make

● Cut the tomato into slices and layer it with the beef, spinach, mustard and black pepper in between the slices of sourdough bread.

Health benefits

Beef is a great source of creatine and lean protein to help you pack on muscle.

Tomato contains plenty of vitamin C, which helps your body form strong tendons, ligaments and bone tissue.

Mustard stimulates circulation and metabolism and helps neutralise toxins in the body.

Find your favourite mustard

English is the classic mustard – hot and packed with flavour, it delivers a sharp kick to the tastebuds. Perfect with British beef.

Dijon is a smooth, medium-strength mustard that originates from the Dijon region of France and provides a tangy kick.

Wholegrain has a sharp, pungent flavour, which can add an extra edge to a roast chicken.

Egg bagel ⓥ

White bagels provide high-GI carbohydrate, which enters your bloodstream fast and drives the protein from the egg into your muscles, helping you to get more from your workout. This is also a vegetarian-friendly lunch.

Ingredients

1 white bagel
3tbsp low-fat mayonnaise
1tbsp Dijon mustard
1 boiled egg, sliced
1 tomato, chopped
1tbsp watercress
A twist of black pepper

To make

● Slice the bagel in half and toast it.

● Mix the mayonnaise with the mustard.

● Cut the hard-boiled egg and tomato into thin slices.

● Layer the mustard mayo, egg tomato and watercress between the two halves of the bagel.

Health benefits

Egg contains all the crucial amino acids that your hardworking muscles need to build and repair themselves.

Watercress is a great source of energy-promoting iron and bone-building calcium.

Tomato provides vitamin C, which contributes to your amino acid metabolism, helping the body form new muscle.

Nutritional value
265 **calories**
32g **carbs**
20g **protein**
7g **fat**

Turkey bagel

Wholemeal bagels are packed with high-quality carbs that will keep your glycogen levels topped up and provide a sustained energy boost, making them great as a pre-workout lunch.

Ingredients

1 wholemeal bagel
2 thick slices of turkey
½ red pepper, sliced
1 tomato, sliced
A handful of rocket

To make

● Slice the bagel in half and toast it.

● Cut the red pepper and tomato into thin slices.

● Layer the rocket, turkey, tomato and red pepper in between the two halves of the bagel.

Health benefits

Turkey is a lean way to pack on muscle, thanks to its protein content. It's also rich in immunity-boosting selenium.

Red pepper is full of potassium, a nutrient that helps to ensure proper muscle growth.

Rocket is a great source of cancer-fighting phytochemicals such as thiocyanates and sulforaphane.

Meaty alternatives

Meat	Portion size	Protein	Fat	Calories
Pork	100g	29.2g	13.7g	240
Beef	100g	23.6g	14.2g	243
Chicken	100g	25g	2g	114

Nutritional value
224 **calories**
34g **carbs**
18g **protein**
5g **fat**

Basque chicken

Bored with eating chicken all the time? Then try spicing it up with peppers and chorizo to reinvigorate your weekly diet. This Basque recipe provides plenty of protein to help you build muscle.

Ingredients (serves 2)

4 chicken legs
50g chorizo, sliced
1 onion, chopped
1 red pepper, sliced
1tbsp olive oil
2 cloves garlic, crushed
400g canned chopped tomatoes
1tsp herbs de Provence
570ml chicken stock
1tbsp plain flour
Black pepper and cayenne pepper to season
A handful of new potatoes
A handful of parsley

To make

● Heat the oil in a pan and cook the chorizo until softened. Then add the chicken and fry on both sides until golden brown. Remove from the pan.

● Add the onion, garlic and peppers and potatoes in the pan and cook until softened.

● Return the meat to the pan and stir in the flour, chicken stock, tomatoes and herbs.

● Season to taste and leave to simmer on the hob on a low heat for 1 hour.

● Garnish with parsley and serve.

Health benefits

Chicken provides plenty of vitamin B6, which aids muscle growth and development.

Chorizo is a great source of protein and a host of vitamins including A, C and E.

Cayenne pepper will fire up your metabolism and help you burn more calories.

Nutritional value
647 **calories**
63g **carbs**
43g **protein**
22g **fat**

Lemon chicken couscous

Training in the evening can often lead to eating late. This light, healthy dinner is perfect if you don't want to go to bed feeling bloated. The chicken will provide you with plenty of post-workout protein too.

Ingredients (serves 2)

2 pre-cooked chicken breasts, sliced
½ a lemon, zest and juice
1tbsp olive oil
150g couscous
150g baby plum tomatoes, halved
50g sunflower seeds
A handful of coriander

To make

● Combine the olive oil, chicken and lemon juice and zest, and refrigerate for 15 minutes.

● Put the couscous in a bowl, pour one cup of boiling water over it and leave for 10 minutes. When the water is fully absorbed, fluff up the couscous with a fork.

● Add the tomatoes, seeds and half the coriander to the couscous.

● Place the chicken on top, along with the remaining marinade and the rest of the coriander.

Health benefits

Lemon juice is packed with immunity boosting vitamin C and cancer-fighting flavonols.

Baby plum tomatoes contain high levels of betacarotene and lycopene, which reduce inflammation and muscle soreness.

Sunflower seeds are a top source of vitamin E, which helps to neutralise potentially damaging free radicals in the body.

Nutritional value
551 **calories**
48g **carbs**
54g **protein**
15g **fat**

Chicken noodles

Egg noodles are a great basis for a muscle-building dinner. As well as protein, they also provide carbs to replenish your glycogen stores and give you energy after a hard workout.

Ingredients

150g chicken breast
2tsp olive oil
50g (dry weight) egg noodles
75g sugar snap peas
1 carrot, grated
2tbsp orange juice
3tsp soy sauce
1tsp rapeseed oil
1 small piece of fresh ginger, chopped
1tsp sesame seeds

To make

● Slice the chicken into strips and stir-fry with olive oil until cooked through.

● Soak the noodles for 4-5 minutes in boiling water until soft. Allow to cool while you grate the carrot.

● Mix the orange juice, soy sauce, oil, ginger and sesame seeds.

● Mix the dressing with the chicken and noodles, then add the grated carrot and sugar snap peas and mix again.

Health benefits

Chicken delivers a dose of carnitine, an amino acid that helps the body use fat as energy and helps the muscles remove toxins.

Carrot is packed with betacarotene, which the body transforms into vitamin A to strengthen the immune system.

Sugar snap peas are packed with antioxidants that will help to banish muscle pain and inflammation.

Nutritional value
607 **calories**
47g **carbs**
42g **protein**
16g **fat**

Chicken stir-fry

Eating chicken stir-fry from your local Chinese takeaway won't help you build muscle, but this home-cooked version will do the job just fine. Chicken is an excellent source of lean protein and vitamin B3, which helps to prevent fat storage.

Ingredients

2 chicken breasts, cut into strips
50g brown rice
A handful of broccoli florets
½ a red pepper, sliced
1 small piece of ginger
1tbsp soy sauce
1tbsp sesame oil

To make

● Steam the broccoli for five minutes and place to one side.

● Heat a wok or a large non-stick frying pan over a medium heat and coat the bottom with the sesame oil.

● Place the chicken strips in the pan and cook for 5 minutes, turning occasionally.

● Add the pepper and ginger and cook for a further 3 minutes.

● Add the broccoli, stir in the soy sauce and cook for a further minute.

● Cook the rice according to the packaging instructions and serve with the stir-fried chicken and veg.

Health benefits

Broccoli is high in chromium, which enables the body to build muscle, reduce body fat and produce energy.

Ginger contains an acidic substance that boosts metabolism by up to 20%, helping you to burn fat more quickly.

Soy sauce helps to lower cholesterol and is full of antioxidants – just make sure you buy the low-sodium variety.

Nutritional value
648 **calories**
79g **carbs**
39g **protein**
8g **fat**

Jamaican jerk chicken

In addition to helping you build muscle, the protein in this Caribbean dish – combined with its high fibre content – will keep you feeling full for longer and help you resist the urge to snack between meals.

Ingredients

2 chicken breasts
½ onion, chopped
1 jalapeño pepper, seeded and diced
½tsp allspice, ground
½tsp dried thyme
½tsp cayenne pepper
½tsp black pepper
½tsp sage
½tsp nutmeg
½tsp cinnamon
1 clove garlic, crushed
½tbsp white wine vinegar
85g wholemeal rice

To make

● Combine the allspice, thyme, cayenne pepper, black pepper, sage, nutmeg, cinnamon and garlic. Then add the vinegar, jalapeño pepper and onion and mix well.

● Marinate the chicken breasts in the mixture for 1 hour.

● Remove the chicken and baste with the marinade mix. Grill the breasts for 10 minutes on each side or until they are fully cooked and the juices run clear.

● Serve with the rice, cooked according to packaging instructions.

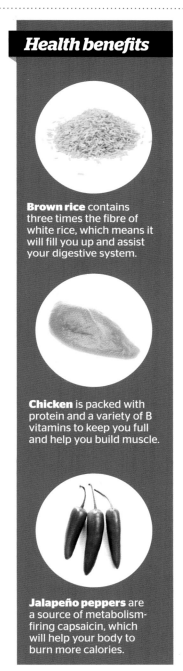

Health benefits

Brown rice contains three times the fibre of white rice, which means it will fill you up and assist your digestive system.

Chicken is packed with protein and a variety of B vitamins to keep you full and help you build muscle.

Jalapeño peppers are a source of metabolism-firing capsaicin, which will help your body to burn more calories.

Nutritional value
718.5 **calories**
31g **carbs**
45g **protein**
23g **fat**

Pork stew

This hearty pork stew is positively packed with protein, making it an ideal dinner for building muscle after a hard session in the gym.

Ingredients

225g lean shoulder of pork, diced
A sprinkle of sugar
½ clove garlic, chopped
30ml sherry
300ml stock
4 new potatoes
1 spring onion, chopped
150g spinach leaves
Salt and freshly ground pepper to taste

To make

● Arrange the pork in the base of a lidded casserole dish.

● Mix the sugar, garlic and chillies with the sherry and stock, stir well and pour over the pork.

● Add the veg, then place the casserole on the hob and bring it to a gentle simmer.

● Put the lid on and simmer over a gentle heat for 90 minutes, stirring occasionally.

Health benefits

Pork provides plenty of muscle-building protein as well as magnesium, which helps to keep muscles strong.

Potatoes will keep your glycogen levels topped up so your body doesn't use its protein stores for fuel.

Spinach is rich in vitamin C, folate and betacarotene – all needed for a healthy immune system – as well as bone-building calcium.

Alcohol alternatives

Guinness Packed with iron and even a hint of protein, Guinness has a uniquely dark creamy flavour, with a subtle, tangy aftertaste.

Cider Whether brewed from apples or pears, cider gives a sharp, refreshingly fruity kick.

Red wine Shiraz has a warm peppery flavour, while Merlot is a softer option that goes with pretty much anything.

Nutritional Value
678 **calories**
4g **carbs**
62g **protein**
23g **fat**

Beef steak

Nothing beats beef for building muscle. As well as protein, it has plenty of creatine, which increases muscle mass, decreases body fat and improves endurance. It also contains CLA, an unsaturated fatty acid that has been shown to reduce body fat stores.

Ingredients

1 large fillet steak
A handful of broccoli florets
A handful of cauliflower florets
1 garlic clove, crushed
1tbsp olive oil

To make

● Steam the broccoli and cauliflower for five minutes.

● Heat the olive oil in a frying pan and add the garlic.

● Cook the steak in the pan according to preference (2-3 minutes each side for rare, 4-5 for medium rare, 8-9 for medium, 12 for well done)

● Rest the steak for at least 5 minutes

Health benefits

Cauliflower is high in iron, which provides energy to your muscles and folate, which helps produce and maintain new muscle cells.

Broccoli is high in chromium, which the body needs to build muscle, reduce body fat and produce energy.

Garlic protects blood vessels from oxidative stress and can help to lower cholesterol.

Choice cuts

Sirloin is usually tender and tasty, and the fat sits on top of the steak so it can be trimmed easily.

T-bone comes from the thicker end of the spine, meaning you get more bone and less meat.

Rump can be fairly tough, but it's cheaper than fillet and has a lot more flavour.

Home-made chilli burger

If you only eat burgers at McDonald's, then you're missing out. Home-made burgers can be far healthier – not to mention tastier – and they're surprisingly straightforward to prepare.

Ingredients

220g lean steak mice
1tbsp olive oil
½ onion, diced
½ chilli, chopped
A pinch of black pepper
2 slices of tomato
A handful of baby spinach leaves
1 slice of cheddar
2 sweet potatoes
1 wholemeal burger bun

To make

● Peel the sweet potatoes, cut them into wedges, toss them in olive oil and roast them in the oven on 200˚C for 20 minutes, turning them halfway through.

● Mix the mince, onion, chilli and black pepper and shape it into a burger.

● Cut the tomato and cheese slices and wash the spinach leaves.

● Grill the burger at 180°C until cooked to your preference, turning it halfway through.

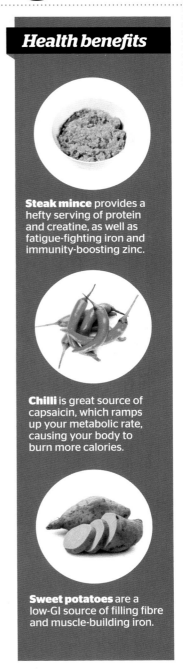

Health benefits

Steak mince provides a hefty serving of protein and creatine, as well as fatigue-fighting iron and immunity-boosting zinc.

Chilli is great source of capsaicin, which ramps up your metabolic rate, causing your body to burn more calories.

Sweet potatoes are a low-GI source of filling fibre and muscle-building iron.

Nutritional value
822 **calories**
63g **carbs**
54g **protein**
32g **fat**

Spaghetti bolognese

Ready-made supermarket sauces tend to contain excessive salt and sugar, which is why you're much better off making your own at home. This bolognese recipe offers a healthy and tasty take on a classic Italian dish.

Ingredients

175g lean minced beef
1 small onion, finely chopped
1 clove of garlic, crushed
225g canned tomatoes
2tbsp olive oil
2tbsp tomato purée
1tsp dried basil
1tsp paprika
1tsp oregano
A pinch of black pepper
50g wholemeal spaghetti

To make

● Heat the oil in a saucepan, then gently cook the onion and garlic for 5 minutes until soft.

● Increase the heat, then add the mince and brown, stirring frequently.

● Once the meat has browned, add the purée, tomatoes, basil, paprika, oregano and black pepper.

● Cover the sauce and simmer gently for 20 minutes, then simmer for a further 20 minutes with the lid off.

● Cook the spaghetti according to packaging instructions.

Health benefits

Minced beef provides a rich supply of lean protein and creatine for building muscle.

Tomatoes are a great source of betacarotene, which heals muscle tissue damage and boosts the immune system.

Garlic can help to lower cholesterol and protect blood vessels from the oxidative stress casued by exercise.

Nutritional value
473 **calories**
61g **carbs**
33g **protein**
36g **fat**

Moroccan lamb stew

Lamb is an excellent basis for a muscle-building meal. As well as protein, it's also rich in the essential amino acid tryptophan, which helps to regulate appetite. This Middle Eastern dish combines lamb with herbs and spices to great effect.

Ingredients (serves 2)

200g lamb shoulder, cubed
2tbsp olive oil
1 onion, chopped
2 garlic cloves, chopped
½tsp paprika
½tsp ground cinnamon
½tsp turmeric
½tsp ground allspice
½tsp ground coriander
½tsp ground nutmeg
1tsp cardamon
Pinch of black pepper
550ml stock
Handful of raisins
Handful of dried apricots
2 carrots, sliced
200g canned chopped tomatoes
1tbsp fresh coriander leaves, chopped
1tbsp fresh parsley, chopped
150g couscous

To make

● Heat 1tbsp of olive oil in a large saucepan. Add half the meat and brown, then transfer to a plate. Brown the rest of the meat in the same way and remove from the pan.

● Heat the remaining oil in the pan and fry the onion for about 5 minutes until soft.

● Return the meat to the pan with the garlic, tomatoes, stock, spices, raisins, apricots and black pepper.

● Bring to the boil, then simmer for 1½-2 hours until the meat is tender.

● Add the carrots 15 minutes before the end of the cooking time and the parsley and coriander before serving.

● Cook the couscous according to packaging instructions and serve with the stew.

Health benefits

Parsley is a great source of folic acid, which helps to boost your cardiovascular system.

Paprika is high in capsaicin, which fires your metabolism and helps it to burn more calories.

Cinnamon is high in antioxidants that reduce post-workout muscle inflammation. It also helps to regulate blood sugar.

Nutritional value
623.5 **calories**
25g **carbs**
54g **protein**
30g **fat**

Lamb casserole

All the carbs in this meaty casserole are slow-release, which means they'll keep your insulin levels steady and stop you needing to snack between meals. It also provides plenty of muscle-building protein.

Ingredients

2 lamb fillets, cubed
1tbsp olive oil
½ an onion, chopped
1 garlic clove, chopped
½tsp paprika
550ml stock
1 bay leaf
50g broad beans
½tbsp fresh parsley, chopped

To make

● Heat half the olive oil in a large flameproof casserole. Add half the meat and brown, then transfer to a plate. Brown the rest of the meat in the same way and remove from the casserole.

● Heat the remaining oil in the pan and fry the onion for about 5 minutes until soft.

● Return the meat to the casserole with the garlic, bay leaf, paprika and stock, and season with salt and pepper.

● Bring to the boil, and then simmer for 1-1½ hours until the meat is tender.

● Add the broad beans 10 minutes before the end of the cooking time and add the parsley before serving.

Health benefits

Lamb is packed with protein and the essential amino acid tryptophan, which helps to regulate your appetite.

Onion is a great source of chromium, a mineral that helps to control insulin response.

Broad beans contain plenty of filling fibre and muscle-building protein.

Nutritional value
620.5 **calories**
32g **carbs**
24g **protein**
32g **fat**

Salmon and pesto pasta

Swapping white pasta for the wholemeal variety is a great way to enjoy this Italian dish without consuming a bowlful of refined carbohydrates in the process. Wholemeal pasta is also a great source of filling fibre.

Ingredients

1 salmon fillet
1tbsp pesto
1tbsp olive oil
½ a red onion, chopped
4 cherry tomatoes, chopped
75g wholemeal pasta

To make

● Heat the oil in a pan and lightly fry the salmon and onion for 5 minutes, flipping the salmon fillet halfway through.

● Add the tomatoes and cook for a further 2 minutes, stirring throughout.

● Remove all ingredients from the pan and cut the salmon fillets into chunks.

● Cook the pasta according to manufacturer's instructions.

● Mix the ingredients in with pasta and pesto and serve.

Health benefits

Salmon This oily fish is full of muscle-building protein and omega 3 fatty acids, which help to reduce inflammation after exercise.

Red onion is an excellent source of chromium, a mineral that helps to control insulin response and curb sugar cravings.

Cherry tomatoes contain high levels of the antioxidant lycopene and a healthy dose of immunity-boosting vitamin C.

Nutritional value
413 **calories**
30g **carbs**
21g **protein**
26g **fat**

Salmon fillet

After a punishing workout, few foods can soothe your aching muscles like salmon. Its omega 3 fatty acids reduce inflammation and help you recover faster. Salmon is also a great muscle-building food, full of high-quality protein and essential amino acids.

Ingredients

1 large salmon fillet
1tbsp pesto
6 new potatoes
A handful of broccoli
1tbsp lemon juice

To make

● Preheat your oven to 180°C.

● Spread the pesto across the top of the salmon fillet and place it on a baking tray in the oven for 10-15 minutes until the pesto forms a crust and the salmon is cooked through.

● Boil the new potatoes in a pan for 10-12 minutes until soft and steam the broccoli for 5 minutes.

● Pour the lemon juice over the salmon and then serve.

Health benefits

Pesto is made from olive oil and pine nuts, which contain unsaturated fats that help to break down fat stored in the body.

Lemon juice helps to control your blood sugar levels, which prevents fat storage and stops you craving sugary food.

Potatoes contain starch, which helps your body burn calories and keeps you feeling full by slowing down the digestive process.

Nutritional value
712 **calories**
54g **carbs**
36g **protein**
35g **fat**

Grilled mackerel

Eating oily fish such as mackerel is a great way to boost your muscle-building efforts. In addition to providing plenty of protein, oily fish are also high in omega 3 fatty acids, which help to reduce muscle inflammation after a hard workout.

Ingredients

115g mackerel
75g quinoa
10g butter
½ a lemon, sliced
2tsp extra virgin olive oil
15g mixed seeds
1 red pepper, sliced
1 courgette, sliced

To make

● Soak the quinoa in hot water for five minutes, then drain and rinse.

● Place the quinoa in water (twice as much as the quinoa) and bring to the boil. Reduce the heat and simmer for 20 minutes.

● Wrap the mackerel, lemon slices and butter in foil and place under a medium grill in a small baking tray, then brush the pepper and courgette with olive oil and add to the simmering quinoa just before the end of cooking.

● Serve the mackerel on the quinoa, with the courgette and pepper on the side.

● Squeeze a little lemon juice over it and sprinkle with the seeds.

Health benefits

Quinoa is a high-protein grain-like seed that contains manganese and magnesium, which aid muscle relaxation and glucose absorption.

Seeds contain fibre and protein, which help build and repair muscle tissue.

Red pepper is high in vitamin C, which helps lower cortisol, a muscle-wasting hormone that increases with weight training.

Nutritional value

736 **calories**
43g **carbs**
42g **protein**
36g **fat**

Baked cod fillet

Cod doesn't have to be served in batter with chips after a Friday night spent in the pub. This healthy cod recipe offers a host of benefits to help you build muscle and lose weight, and it's easy to prepare too.

Ingredients

1 large cod fillet
½ a can of coconut milk
100g steamed broccoli
100g chopped carrots
50g brown rice

To make

● Preheat your oven to 180°C/Gas Mark 4.

● Place the cod fillet and coconut milk in a deep baking dish.

● Bake uncovered for 10 minutes.

● Steam the broccoli and carrots for 5-10 minutes until soft.

● Cook the rice according to packaging instructions and serve with the fish and veg.

Health benefits

Cod has plenty of high-quality protein and omega 3 fatty acids, which help reduce muscle-protein breakdown.

Coconut milk can raise your metabolic rate, which helps your body to burn more calories.

Carrots contain betacarotene, which the body transforms into vitamin K to help strengthen bones.

Fillet your fish

Step 1 Cut about halfway through the thickness of the fish behind the gills

Step 2 Slice a slit roughly 10cm long along the top.

Step 3 Use the tip of the knife to lift the flesh off the bones.

Step 4 Cut the fillet away by sliding the blade along the bone.

Step 5 Use tweezers to remove any remaining large bones from the fillet.

Nutritional value

673 **calories**
40g **carbs**
63g **protein**
19g **fat**

Tuna satay skewers

Tuna is an excellent muscle-building food. In addition to providing plenty of protein, it's also a great source of testosterone-boosting zinc and selenium, which kills off harmful free-radicals that interfere with muscle growth.

Ingredients

250g tuna steak, cubed
½tbsp olive oil
1tbsp rice vinegar
1tbsp fresh ginger, diced
1 garlic clove, crushed
1tbsp peanut butter
250ml fish stock
½tbsp low-sodium soy sauce
½tbsp chilli sauce
Juice of a lime
½ a bag of mixed stir-fry vegetables
200g egg noodles

To make

● Add the oil to a pan and warm it on a medium heat.

● Cook the ginger and garlic for 1 minute and then add the peanut butter, fish stock and soy sauce and leave to simmer for 10 minutes.

● Add the lime juice and chilli sauce and remove it from the heat.

● Thread the tuna cubes on 4 satay skewers and heat for 4 minutes on a grill pan, turning halfway through.

● Use 1tbsp of olive oil in a pan to fry the vegetables for 2 minutes on a medium heat.

● Cook the egg noodles according to packaging instructions.

● Serve the satay sauce with the tuna, noodles and vegetables.

Health benefits

Tuna is a great source of testosterone-boosting zinc and selenium, which kills free radicals that interfere with muscle growth.

Peanut butter is rich in unsaturated fats, which have proven benefits for your heart.

Lime contains plenty of vitamin A and C, which work together to help strengthen your immune system.

Nutritional value

551 **calories**
38g **carbs**
45g **protein**
17g **fat**

Tuna steak

Tuna is ideal for building muscle. Not only is it full of protein, it also contains plenty of selenium – a mineral that helps to kill off harmful free-radicals that interfere with muscle growth – and testosterone-boosting zinc.

Ingredients

1 tuna steak
1tbsp olive oil
1 sweet potato, cut into strips
1 courgette, cut into strips
1 red pepper, cut into strips
1 sprig of rosemary

To make

● Baste the veg with the olive oil and place them on a baking tray in an oven preheated to 220°C/ Gas Mark 7 for 15-20 minutes.

● Grill the tuna steak to preference under a medium heat, turning halfway through.

● Serve with the vegetables and the rosemary.

Health benefits

Courgettes are low in calories and a great source of manganese, which helps the body to process protein.

Red peppers are full of vitamins A and C, which are essential for a healthy immune system and reducing cell damage.

Rosemary is high in dietary fibre, as well as being a good source of calcium, which you need to maintain strong bones.

Alternative veg to roast

Aubergines contain plenty of potassium and dietary fibre.

Parsnips provide an excellent source of manganese, which helps to control blood sugar levels.

Onions contain quercetin, which helps to reduce muscle inflammation.

Nutritional value
623 **calories**
115g **carbs**
23g **protein**
14g **fat**

Thai prawn curry

Curry may have long since overtaken fish and chips as Britain's favourite takeaway, but that shouldn't stop you from making your own at home, especially when they can be this healthy, tasty and easy to cook.

Ingredients (serves 2)

15 fresh prawns without skin
1tbsp olive oil
2 small onions, chopped
2 carrots, chopped
1-2 medium green peppers, chopped
2 fresh tomatoes, chopped
1 garlic clove, crushed or grated
½ a lemongrass stick
1 small piece of ginger, peeled and sliced
2 green chillies, seeded and sliced
1tbsp medium curry powder
½tsp turmeric
6-7 fresh coriander leaves, chopped
3tbsp oyster sauce
½tsp cayenne pepper
1 litre vegetable stock
100ml coconut milk
250g brown rice

To make

● Heat the olive oil in a pan, add the onions and carrots and cook gently for 5 minutes.

● Add the tomatoes, ginger, garlic, cayenne pepper, green chillies, oyster sauce, stock, curry powder, turmeric and coconut milk.

● Simmer for 12-15 minutes to allow the sauce to thicken.

● Cook the rice according to packaging instructions.

● Once cooked, drain the rice and use the water with added lemongrass to blanch the prawns for 3-4 minutes.

● Add the prawns, green peppers and coriander to the sauce and serve.

Health benefits

Prawns contain plenty of protein and vitamin B12 to help you pack on muscle.

Ginger has antibacterial and antioxidant properties that provide a variety of health benefits.

Coconut milk contains lauric acid, which helps to promote a good cardiovascular system.

Nutritional value

561 **calories**
34g **carbs**
35g **protein**
23g **fat**

Mussels

Mussels might seem like an extravagant and indulgent dish, but when prepared and cooked correctly it's actually extremely simple and healthy. Mussels are very high in protein and heart-healthy omega 3 fatty acids.

Ingredients

500g fresh mussels
1tbsp honey
½ an onion, diced
2 garlic cloves, finely chopped
1 small piece of fresh ginger, grated
1 stick of lemongrass, split and bashed
500ml vegetable stock
A handful of coriander leaves, roughly chopped
A large handful of baby leaf spinach
100ml low-fat coconut cream

To make

● Tap each mussel so they close. Discard the ones that don't. Wash the good mussels and remove the beards.

● Add the lemongrass, honey, onions, garlic, ginger and stock. Cover and cook for 6-8 minutes.

● Add the mussels, cover and cook for a further 2-3 minutes. Take off the heat, add the coriander and spinach and leave for 10 minutes.

● Drain the liquid into a pan, add the coconut cream, season with black pepper and keep warm.

● Mix in the mussels and serve

Health benefits

Honey is a great source of iron, which is an essential protein component for metabolism.

Lemongrass is packed with powerful antioxidants that can help to reduce inflammation.

Coriander lowers blood sugar levels, reduces oxidative stress and increases insulin secretion.

Bean stew

Beans are a great alternative to meat – they're full of protein and work equally well in stews and casseroles or even chilli. The borlotti beans used in this recipe also contain cholecystokinin, a natural appetite suppressant.

Ingredients

2tbsp olive oil
2 small onions, chopped
1tsp chopped root ginger
2 garlic cloves, crushed
1tsp fennel seeds
1tsp coriander seeds
1tsp cumin seeds
1tsp ground cinnamon
1 sweet potato, cubed
400g borlotti beans
2 carrots, sliced
½ a celeriac, chopped
250g button mushrooms, halved
2tbsp tomato purée
A handful of fresh parsley
200g (dry weight) Japanese soba noodles

To make

● Heat the oil in a large pan and gently fry the onion, garlic, ginger, cinnamon, fennel seeds, cumin and coriander for 5 minutes.

● Add the potato and cook for a further 4 minutes.

● Add the carrot, celeriac and mushrooms and cook for 1 minute, stirring throughout.

● Stir in the purée, then add enough water to just cover the ingredients.

● Bring to boil and simmer for 20 minutes.

● Add the beans and parsley and cook for 10 minutes.

● Cook the noodles according to packaging instructions and serve with the stew.

Health benefits

Sweet potato contains manganese and copper, which are vital for healthy muscle unction and energy release.

Mushrooms are high in potassium, which helps to convert sugar into energy providing glycogen.

Soba noodles provide plenty of energy and contain twice as much fibre, protein and iron as spaghetti.

Nutritional value

816 **calories**
140g **carbs**
30g **protein**
15g **fat**

Chickpea balti (v)

You don't always need to eat meat to build muscle. This tasty vegetarian curry offers plenty of nutrients that will help you to train harder, recover faster and, most importantly, pack on lean muscle.

Ingredients

1 onion, cut into chunks
A handful of cauliflower florets
1 sweet potato, chopped into 3cm cubes
1 courgette, sliced
1 red pepper, chopped into 3cm chunks
A handful of peas, fresh or frozen
200g canned chickpeas
1tbsp fresh coriander, chopped

For the sauce

1 large onion, chopped
2.5cm root ginger, chopped or grated
1 garlic clove, crushed
4tsp curry paste
400g canned chopped tomatoes
A large handful of coriander, finely chopped

To make

● Sweat the onion, ginger and garlic in a large heavy pan over a medium heat for a few minutes.

● Add the curry paste, tomatoes and coriander and simmer for a further ten minutes. Meanwhile, steam the cauliflower, onion, sweet potato, courgettes and peppers until soft.

● Tip the steamed vegetables into the pan containing the sauce and mix in the peas, chickpeas and coriander.

● Cook gently for a further 5 minutes then serve.

Health benefits

Chickpeas are a good source of muscle-building protein and filling fibre.

Courgettes are a great source of manganese, which helps the body to produce testosterone.

Red peppers are a source of vitamins A and C, which help to reduce the cell damage caused by intense training.

Smoothies

Banana and apple	*120*
Mixed berry with whey	*121*
Mango and orange	*122*
Watermelon and tofu	*123*
Strawberry and oats	*124*

Nutritional value
289 **calories**
64g **carbs**
5g **protein**
6g **fat**

Banana and apple Ⓥ

Bananas are a great post-workout food thanks to their high levels of muscle-soothing potassium, which will relieve your aching limbs after a hard gym session, while apples help you burn fat.

Ingredients

1 banana
1 apple
A pinch of cinnamon
1tbsp honey
2tbsp Greek yoghurt
100ml water

Health benefits

Apple
is rich in the fibre pectin, which helps keep you full and stops cells from storing fat.

Cinnamon
helps reduce blood sugar levels and boosts your levels of insulin to help you lose fat.

Greek yoghurt
contains protein to help you put on muscle along with a decent serving of filling fibre.

Mixed berry with whey

This muscle-building smoothie is packed with plenty of tasty berries. Adding whey protein to a smoothie is a great way to up your daily protein intake while enjoying the health benefits of the fruit.

Ingredients

25g whey protein
80g blueberries
50g blackberries
80g raspberries
100ml water

Health benefits

Blueberries contain pterostilbene, a compound that helps the body to break down fat.

Raspberries are extremely fibrous and packed with bone-strengthening vitamin K.

Blackberries contain pectin, which stabilises your blood sugar and minimises cravings.

Nutritional value

205 **calories**
29g **carbs**
19g **protein**
3g **fat**

Nutritional value
248 **calories**
60g **carbs**
4g **protein**
2g **fat**

Mango and orange ⓥ

Training regularly can severely affect your immune system. Mangoes and oranges are sources of the immunity-boosting vitamins A and C, so this smoothie both supports your training and helps prevent illness.

Ingredients

1 mango
1 orange
A handful of raspberries
2tbsp natural yoghurt
100ml water

Health benefits

Raspberries contain calcium to boost your metabolism and help you burn fat more efficiently.

Oranges contain high levels of dietary fibre to keep you feeling full for longer.

Natural yoghurt is rich in protein to help you pack on muscle and recover faster after a workout.

Watermelon and tofu Ⓥ

Watermelon provides a healthy dose of lycopene, which helps to destroy free radicals, which are damaging by-products of exercise. This smoothie mixes watermelon with seeds, berries and tofu to provide a balanced nutritional snack.

Ingredients

50g watermelon
1tbsp mixed sunflower seeds, pumpkin seeds and flaxseeds
100g tofu, drained and sliced
100g mixed berries
500ml skimmed milk

Health benefits

Seeds
contain omega 3 fats, which are anti-inflammatory and promote fat-burning.

Tofu
contains quality protein, as well as magnesium and calcium for good muscle function.

Berries
have vitamin C that will boost your absorption of calcium from the tofu.

Nutritional Value
331 **calories**
43g **carbs**
25g **protein**
7g **fat**

Nutritional value
470 **calories**
69g **carbs**
20g **protein**
25g **fat**

Strawberry and oat ⓥ

Strawberries are a great source of manganese, a mineral that controls blood sugar levels and reduces the urge to snack – helping to ensure you don't undermine all your hard work in the gym with poor food choices.

Ingredients

20 strawberries
50g porridge oats
350ml milk
1tbsp flaxseed oil

Health benefits

Porridge oats contain protein to help you build muscle and fibre to keep you feeling full.

Milk supplies B vitamins, which help to turn food into energy, as well as protein.

Flaxseed oil provides a large dose of healthy fats that help to reduce inflammation.

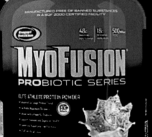

SUPPLEMENT YOUR DIET

Give the 50 meals a bit of help and increase your chances of building a lean and muscular body

The 50 meals in this book contain all the muscle-building nutrients you need to build an impressive physique. But even if you're diet's great, you can always use a little more help to pack on muscle mass, burn fat or protect your body from the rigours of strenuous exercise. That's where supplements come in.

Trouble is, they can be a bit confusing, especially since every supplier claims that its brand is best. But you don't need a degree in chemistry to understand what you're putting into your body. You just need this straightforward guide, which details what you need, when you need it, why you need it, and any potential pitfalls.

So read on to find out how pills and powders can provide all the nutritional back-up you need – and give yourself every chance of sending your training gains through the roof.

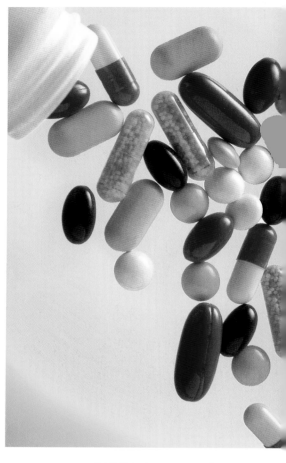

Protein

What is it? Protein makes up part of the structure of every cell and tissue in your body, and makes up an average of 20% of your bodyweight. It's needed to form new tissue as well as body enzymes and various hormones.

What does it do? Protein is broken down for fuel during exercise, so you need a concentrated source of it to supplement your usual intake. Protein supplements should ideally contain high levels of essential amino acids, which are readily digested, absorbed and retained by the body for muscle repair.

Who should take it? All athletes need to compensate for increased breakdown of protein during training, while strength athletes need extra to provide the stimulus for muscle growth.

How much should I take? The Food Standards Authority recommends a daily intake of 55g of protein for adults, but most dieticians agree that isn't enough for anyone training regularly. The International Olympic Committee recommends around 1.2-1.4g of protein per kg of bodyweight a day for endurance athletes or 1.4-1.7g per kg for strength and power athletes.

The basics if you're lean – have less than 10% body fat – then try to have a post-workout shake with 0.6g of protein and 1.2g of carbs per kilo of lean bodyweight. So an 80kg man would need 43.2g of protein and 98.4g of carbs.

If you're above 10% body fat then the formula is the same as above, but with the amino acids L-glycine and L-glutamine in place of the carbs.

That said, if you are a serious athlete then you can't really get too much protein. Some report big benefits when eating upwards of 3g per kg each day, and you won't get fat because any excess your body doesn't need gets flushed out when you pee. The only exception to this is if you have a kidney disease. If not, then eat up in the knowledge that you hard work in the gym is getting the required nutritional support.

When should I take it? The most important thing is to make sure you get some protein early in the post-exercise recovery phase, ideally in the first hour after exercise. Aim to have about 50g of protein and 50g of carbs at 30 and 90 minutes after training.

Does it have any side effects? It used to be thought that excess protein could place excess stress on the liver or kidneys, but this has never been demonstrated on healthy people, only ones already suffering from kidney failure. A high protein intake can potentially cause dehydration, so make sure you're drinking plenty of water, but other than that it won't do you any harm.

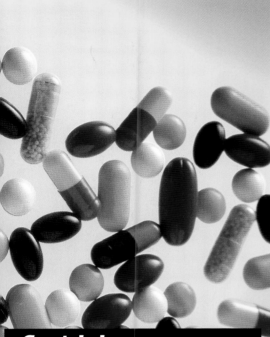

Amino acids

What are they? Branched-chain amino acids (BCAA) supplements contain valine, leucine and isoleucine. These are considered 'essential' amino acids because your body can't produce them so they need to be present in your diet. Together, they can comprise up to one-third of muscle protein.

What do they do? The theory is that they can help prevent the breakdown of muscle tissue during intense exercise. They also increase the release of human growth hormone, which is vital for building muscle.

Who should take them? Anyone who weight trains, preferably in capsule form rather than tablet or liquid. However, there's little evidence that BCAAs will improve performance among endurance athletes, who should get enough BCAAs from a recovery drink to make a separate supplement unnecessary – unless they're training seriously hard.

How much should I take? The science suggests that anything less than 20 capsules per workout is a waste of time. Many professional rugby and football clubs have seen huge improvements in performance using 40 caps of BCAAs every workout.

When should I take them? They work best if taken before, during and after a workout. Studies show that taking BCAA supplements before resistance training reduce muscle soreness, while taking them during and after exercise can reduce muscle breakdown.

Do they have any side effects? BCAAs are fairly safe, since you'd normally find them in protein in your diet anyway. Excessive intake might reduce the absorption of other amino acids, but that's about it.

Creatine

What is it? Creatine is a protein that is made naturally in the body, but can also be found in meat and fish or taken in higher doses as a supplement.

What does it do? It's like a backup generator for the body. There are times when your body can't keep up with energy demand – such as brief periods of all-out effort with little recovery – so it needs another source of phosphates, which creatine can provide. Creatine also promotes protein manufacture and reduce protein breakdown following intense exercise.

Who should take it? People who train with weights or do sports that involve repeated high-intensity movements, such as sprints or jumps. Bodybuilders use it because it increases muscle hypertrophy by drawing water into muscle cells. Evidence does not indicate that creatine benefits endurance athletes.

How much should I take? The average person takes in or produces around 2g of creatine a day, and research shows that anything over 5g is simply excreted. So the best way to top up is with around 3g a day.

When should I take it? Not before a workout because it's hygroscopic, which means it draws water into your stomach and bloodstream from tissues or muscles and can cause muscle cramps or bloating. The ideal time is immediately after your workout.

Does it have any side effects? The main one is weight gain, because of increased muscle tissue and extra water in your muscle cells, so it's not ideal for sports that use weight categories such as boxing. There are also anecdotal reports about stomach pains, dehydration, muscle injury and kidney damage, but there is no clinical evidence to support these stories.

Great shakes
What goes into your post-training protein drink

Whey
The most popular protein shake type, whey, is derived from milk. It's digested quickly, making it useful for post-exercise recovery. It also has a higher concentration of essential amino acids than whole milk, which means it's better for minimising post-exercise muscle breakdown.

Casein
Casein, which makes up 80% of the protein content of milk, is made up of larger protein molecules that provide a slow, steady release of amino acids into the bloodstream. Because of this, many experts say it is the best protein to use before going to sleep at night or for breakfast.

Which should you use after a workout?
If you have to pick one, whey. But you can simply mix whey with milk to get both. After a workout, 250ml of milk mixed with a 25g scoop of whey powder gives a big chunk of fast-acting protein right when you need it, with the added benefit of 16g of slow-acting casein.

What supp? Answering frequently asked questions

Can't I get all the nutrition I need from my daily diet?
Yes, if you really watch what you eat. Having said that, you'll sometimes find that getting the optimum amount of certain substances for your training means eating a lot. For instance, getting the amount of creatine many trainers recommend would mean eating an awful lot of beef. Use supplements to fill the gaps in your diet, but don't rely on them to counteract bad eating habits.

Do I need to take supplements on the days I'm not training?
Short answer: yes. You get stronger as you recover from exercise, so making sure you're getting enough nutrients on your rest days is essential.

Should I be waking up in the middle of the night to take supplements?
Almost definitely not. You might have heard about bodybuilders getting up at 3am to neck a quick shake, but as soon as you're awake for more than three seconds you disrupt the production of melatonin, which is one of the most important hormones in building muscle. You're better off having some slow-digesting protein, such as raw nuts, cottage cheese or a casein shake, before bed.

Are they safe?
Since sports supplements are classified as food, they aren't subject to the same strict manufacturing, safety testing or labelling as licensed medicines so there's no guarantee that they're living up to their claims. The EU says it is planning to introduce stricter guidelines but in the meantime it's up to manufacturers to maintain the quality of their own products. Look for supplements that are ISO17025 certified, which means they've been subjected to rigorous checks during their production.

Can I fail a drugs test from taking supplements?
Maybe. If you're a serious enough sportsman to be tested, you need to be careful. A survey from an International Olympic Committee-accredited laboratory in Cologne analysed 634 supplements and found that 15% of them contained substances that would cause a failed drugs test. If you're concerned, consult a registered nutritionist or dietician before taking supplements.

If I take the right combination of things, can I get ripped without working out?
Sadly, no. Anybody who tells you that a magic formula can give you massive biceps and sculpted abs is fibbing. Eat right, train hard and tailor your supplement use to your goals, and you'll see the results you want.

Antioxidants

What are they? Antioxidant supplements contain varying amounts of nutrients and plant extracts, including betacarotene, vitamins C and E, zinc, copper and magnesium. As well as having a beneficial effect on your general health, antioxidants can also help you recover from sports training.

What do they do? Like nasty things such as smoking, sunburn, stress and pollution, very intense exercise can increase your body's generation of molecules known as free radicals, which can harm cell membranes, disrupt DNA and increase your risk of age-related diseases and cancer. There's evidence that antioxidant supplements can protect against this, although some research suggests that supplements are less effective than getting antioxidants naturally as part of your diet. Evidence that they'll actually help your sports performance is harder to come by.

Who should take it? The jury is out but it has been suggested that, because of the environment and average stress levels, everyone should take some type of antioxidant. They work best if rotated, so try ten days on green tea followed by the same period taking grape seed extract, for example.

How much should I take? The EU recommended daily amount for vitamin C is 60mg and for vitamin E 10mg, but these are levels judged sufficient to support health, and some experts believe they are too low. But supplements are no substitute for proper nutrition so aim to eat at least five portions of fruit and vegetables daily – the more intense the colour, the higher the antioxidant content. Including as many different coloured fruits and vegetables as possible ensures you get the widest variety of antioxidants.

When should I take them? This depends on the supplement you're taking and the effect you're looking for. Vitamin C is the antioxidant best taken after a workout because it blocks cortisol, a stress hormone that reduces your muscle-building potential and can encourage fat storage. A 2008 study suggested that antioxidants are most beneficial when taken with meals but the evidence isn't conclusive.

Do they have any side effects? There are side effects related to excessive consumption of certain vitamins found in antioxidant supplements – massive amounts of carotene can turn your skin temporarily orange, for example. Also, the antioxidant minerals zinc, magnesium and copper can be toxic in large doses. If you stick to the recommended dosage, though, you'll be fine.

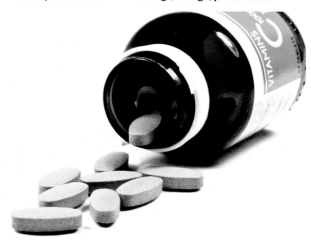

Fat burners

What are they? Also known as thermogenics, these are blends of herbs and stimulants that slightly increase your body temperature, which can help you burn more calories during exercise. Ephedrine, a synthetic version of the Chinese herb ephedra, used to be a key ingredient in these, but it's now only available on prescription in the UK thanks to its harmful side effects and addictive qualities.

What do they do? Some simply burn calories as heat. Others also claim to stimulate the release of adrenaline, increase your metabolic rate or act as appetite suppressants. The evidence for them working is limited, however, and a high-protein diet with regular exercise is likely to produce better weight-loss results in the long term.

Who should take them? Fat burners raise cortisol – a stress hormone – so in some cases they can increase abdominal fat due to the person's already high stress levels. In extreme cases they can cause the adrenal system to get wiped out. If you think you need them, consult your doctor first.

When should I take them? Most contain caffeine and will make you jittery, so the morning's probably best, and never take fat burners after 2pm because they affect sleep patterns. Other than that, go with the recommendation on the bottle.

How much should I take? Again, follow the instructions on the bottle, but they should not be used over a long period of time.

Do they have any side effects? Taking very high doses of ephedrine can have serious effects, including palpitations, anxiety, insomnia, vomiting and dizziness. While herbal alternatives are generally safer, you may get side effects with high doses – some can raise blood pressure or cause heart disturbances.

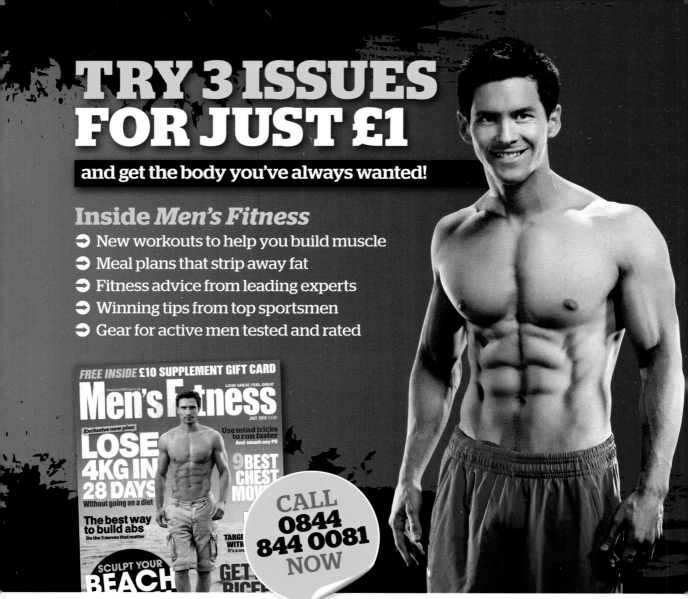